MEGAN KEARNEY'S

BEAUTY
AND
THE BEAST

For Laura
likewise enchanted

Beauty and The Beast: Act Two
Copyright © 2016 Megan Kearney
All rights reserved

Published by The Quietly
First Canadian Edition

Library and Archives Canada Cataloguing in Publication

Kearney, Megan, 1986-, author, illustrator
Megan Kearney's Beauty and The Beast. Act two.

Based on the works of Gabrielle-Suzanne Barbot de Villeneuve
and Jeanne-Marie Leprince de Beaumont.

ISBN 978-0-9937212-1-2 (pbk.)

1. Graphic novels. I. Title. II. Title: Beauty and The Beast.
Act Two.

PN6733.K42M42 2014   *741.5'971*   *C2014-902234-4*

·ACT TWO·

BEAUTY
and The
BEAST

ARE YOU CERTAIN OF WHAT YOU'RE ASKING?

AN EXCHANGE OF EQUIVILENT VALUE IS REQUIRED, AND THE PRICE IS STEEP.

·ENTR'ACTE·

...IT'S NOTHING. NOT FOR SOMETHING LIKE THIS.

•ACT TWO•
CHAPTER ONE

Dark Geranium, Hazel, Agrimony

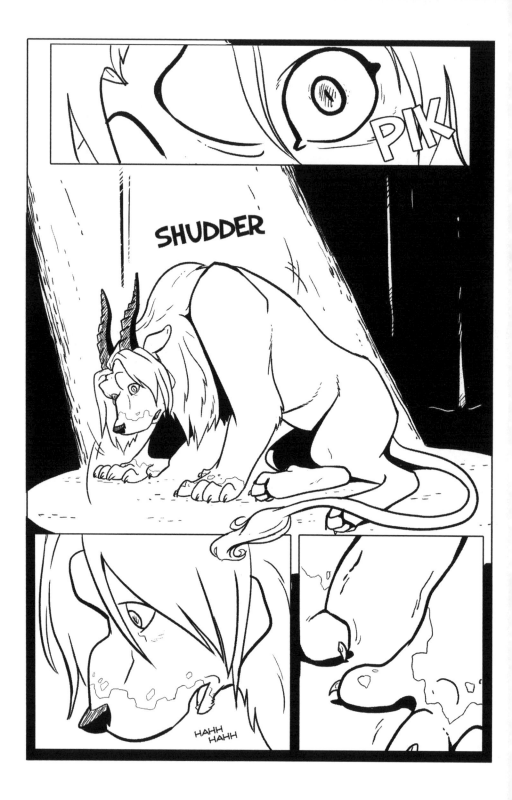

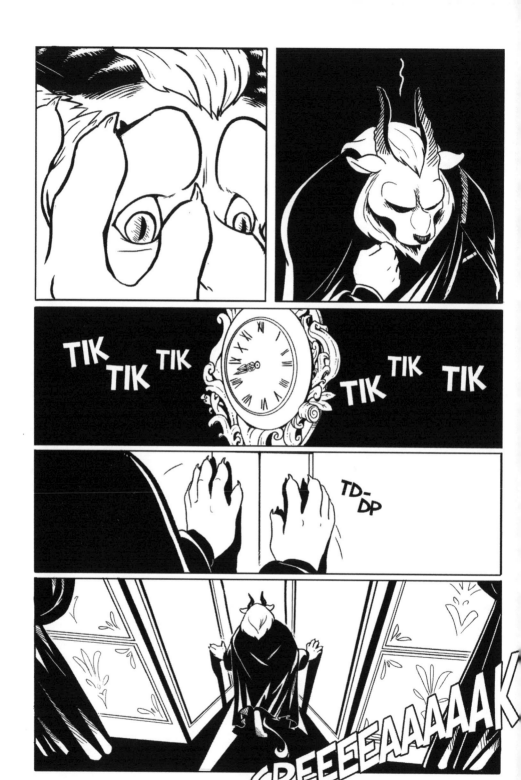

IS THIS HOW IT'S GOING TO BE?

YOU SKULKING IN THE SHADOWS AND ME EATING ALONE?

BECAUSE THAT'S NOT ALL RIGHT.

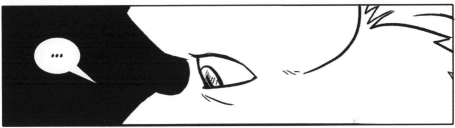

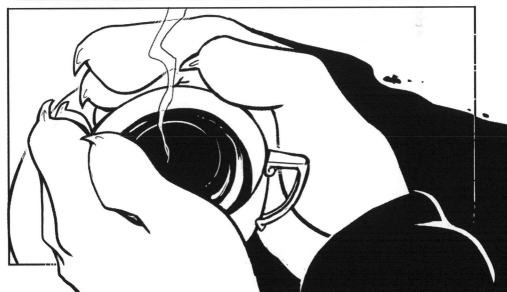

CHAPTER ONE: END

•ACT TWO•
CHAPTER TWO

Hydrangea, Acacia, Oats

IT FEELS LIKE THE MORNING AFTER A STORM.

PLIP

THERE'S AN AIR OF CALM. A SORT OF FRESHNESS.

A SENSE OF THINGS HAVING BEEN SCOURED CLEAN BY THE RAIN.

TWITTER TWEET

TWEET

PAD PAD

AND I FEEL...

...I FEEL...

...GRATEFUL.

CHAPTER TWO: END

•ACT TWO•
CHAPTER THREE

Houstonia, Lilac, Daffodil

I THOUGHT I WOULD FIND YOU HOLED UP HERE

BUT IT SEEMS YOU'VE FOUND SOMETHING ELSE TO OCCUPY YOUR TIME OF LATE.

...WHAT DO YOU NEED OF ME?

MUST I NEED SOMETHING? I SEE YOU SO RARELY.

IT'S AS IF YOU WERE AVOIDING ME.

SHFF

...BUT YOU WOULD NEVER DO THAT, NOW, WOULD YOU?

...

I WAS SHORT A FEW INGREDIENTS FOR AN INFUSION

NOTHING YOU'LL MISS.

TP

TP

.... I DON'T CARE IF YOU AMUSE YOURSELF WITH THAT GIRL, BUT DON'T THINK FOR A MOMENT IT CAN BE ANYTHING MORE THAN THAT, DO YOU UNDERSTAND?

...SAY, WHAT KIND OF BUSHES ARE THESE?

SHUFF

SHUFF

WHAT'S WRONG?!

MMF-- --IT'S NOTHING-- THERE ARE THORNS. I CUT MY HAND.

IS IT VERY DEEP? LET ME SEE.

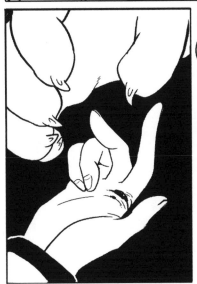

THAT'S IN NEED OF TENDING. ...YARROW, MARIGOLD, AND COMFREY WOULD DO, I THINK.

WILL YOU WAIT HERE A MOMENT?

UH... SURE, BUT...

TP-TP

...IT'S REALLY NOT THAT BAD.

ZASH ZASH ZASH

...

HUUUU~ RUSTLE RUSTLE

HWOOOOOOOOO

...I LIKED YOUR LILACS AND AMARANTHS BETTER.

AS DO I. LET'S HEAD BACK. WE'LL TEND TO YOUR HAND.

SHE IS CONTRACTED TO *ME*. **NOT** TO YOU.

SNARRRLLL.

RUSTLE RUSTLE RUSTLE

ZSH

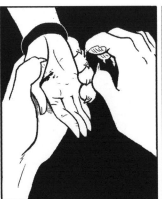
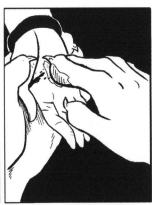

THERE. LET'S BIND THAT UP AND LET IT HEAL.

HM.

DAMN IT.

I CAN'T TIE IT OFF. I'M SORRY.

IT'S FINE--

YOU WERE HURT BECAUSE OF ME, AND I'M TOO CLUMSY TO ACCOMPLISH EVEN THIS SMALL THING TO SET IT RIGHT--

....MAY I?

OH, OF COURSE YOU CAN KEEP THE B--

Chapter Thre

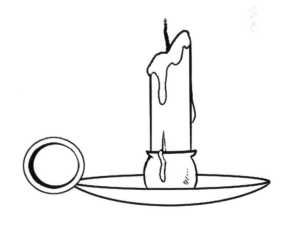

•ACT TWO•
CHAPTER FOUR

Sainfoin, Zinnia, Iris

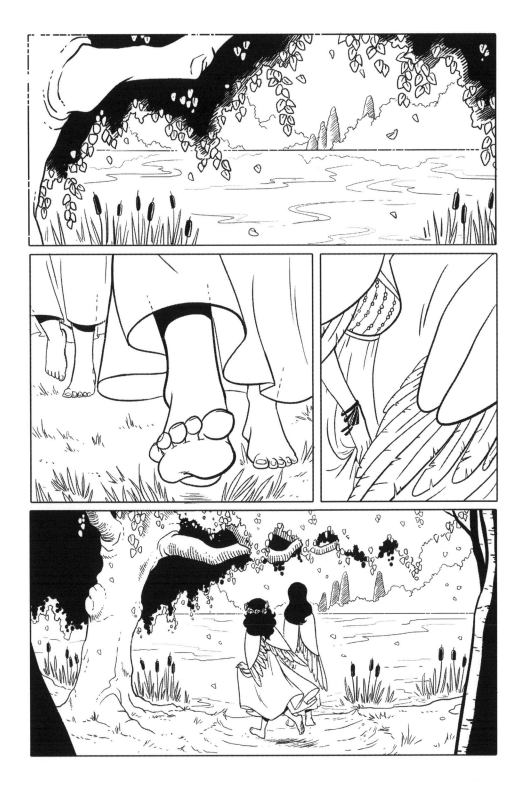

ARE YOU COMING?

TUG

HIIIN

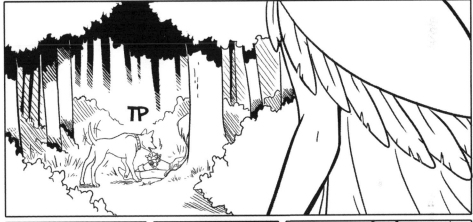

ZASH

ZASH
ZASH

ZASH
ZASH

AAAH!

AA--!

OH.

OH, I DIDN'T EVEN THINK--

BEAUTY, I DIDN'T KNOW, IT DIDN'T OCCUR TO ME THAT YOU MIGHT WANT...AH, I'M A FOOL.

SNUFF

...BUT THIS I CAN REMEDY, IF NOTHING ELSE. WE'LL SEE TO IT RIGHT NOW.

HUP

SPLOOSH SPLASH

TP
TP

...

BLOOP.
BLOOP.

OH! IT'S WORKING!

I'LL LEAVE YOU TO THEM, THEN.

WAIT

...STAY.

I... I SHOULDN'T... THIS SORT OF THING IS PRIVATE, ISN'T IT? FAMILY BUSINESS?

...PLEASE.

"BUT GIANT," SAID THE CLEVER PRINCESS "HOW IS IT THAT SEVEN PRINCES HAVE STRUCK YOU DOWN, AND YET YOU DO NOT DIE?"

THE TERRIBLE GIANT LAUGHED "CLEVER PRINCESS, IT IS BECAUSE I HAVE NO HEART IN MY BODY. I HAVE HIDDEN IT AT THE BOTTOM OF THE DRY OLD WELL!"

SO, THAT NIGHT, THE CLEVER PRINCESS WENT OUT AND DUG UP THE OLD WELL, BUT SHE DID NOT FIND THE GIANT'S HEART...

CREAK CREAK

TK

WEH WEH-EH

ARE WE ALL DONE, SWEETIE? OOH, SOMEONE IS TIRED!

WEH! WEH!

YOUR MOTHER USED TO TELL THAT STORY WHEN YOU GIRLS WERE SMALL.

WEH-EH! WEH!

OH, RIGHT... I'D SORT OF FORGOTTEN...

WELL, THAT'S IT FOR STORYTIME TONIGHT, I'M AFRAID!

PAT PAT

YOU TAKE A REST, MY DEAR. I'LL PUT HIM TO BED.

OH, THANK YOU, PAPA!

SH-SH-SH THERE'S A GOOD LITTLE LAD, EH?

HNN!

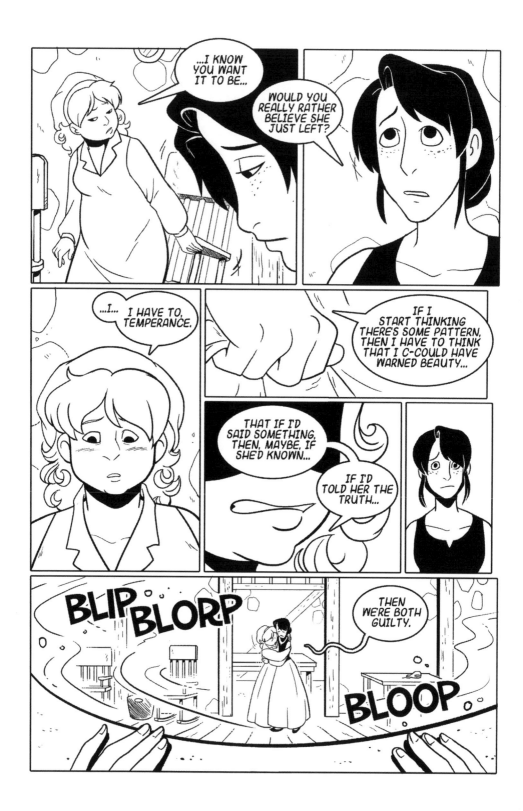

I... I'M HAPPY THEY'RE WELL, BUT...

...I WANT THEM TO NEED ME, BUT I HATE TO SEE THEM HURTING.

I WANT THEM TO THINK OF ME, BUT I DON'T W-WANT THEM BLAMING THEMSELVES

I HATE THAT I'M SO SELFISH.

AND I DON'T UNDERSTAND WHAT VIRTUE AND TEMPERANCE WERE TALKING ABOUT

R-ROSES AND LIES AND BEING G-GUILTY

PLASH PLASH

...I THINK I MAY.

PLASH

PLASH

YOU... YOU DO?

SNF

HM...

Chapter Four: End

•ACT TWO•
CHAPTER FIVE

Calendula, Petunia, Jonqui🍃

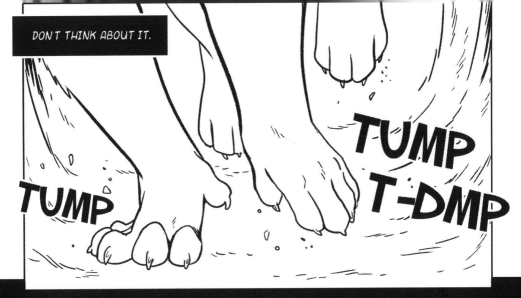

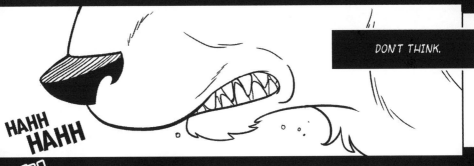

THUMP

PLIP

SHAHHHHHHHH

...

PLEASE...

...YOU'RE TOUCHING ME LIKE YOU WOULD TOUCH AN ANIMAL.

BEAST, YOU KNOW I DON'T.

...DO YOU WANT ME TO STOP?

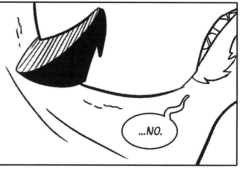

...

...NO.

CHAPTER FIVE: END

•ACT TWO•
CHAPTER SIX

Spanish Jasmine, Oleander, Enchanter's Nightshade

...IT'S, UH...IT'S BEEN A VERY LONG TIME SINCE I LAST WOKE BESIDE SOMEONE.

PFFT HA HA HA! WELL, YOU CERTAINLY SNORE LESS THAN MY SISTERS!

OH, THE RAIN HAS STOPPED

...FOR NOW.

WE MUST HAVE SLEPT FOR HOURS.

THE SUN IS GOING DOWN, TOO.

...INSTEAD OF DWELLING ON WHAT CAN NEVER BE CHANGED, PERHAPS I OUGHT TO EMBRACE WHAT'S IN FRONT OF ME NOW?

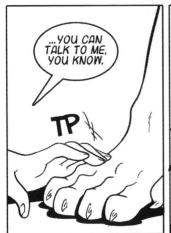

...YOU CAN TALK TO ME, YOU KNOW.

TP

I'M NOT ASKING FOR THE THINGS YOU'D BE COMPROMISING YOURSELF TO SAY.

BUT THE REST...I'M HERE. I'M LISTENING.

...THE TRUTH IS, I'M AFRAID

AFRAID?

TP TP TP TP TP

ARE YOU WELL?

TUMP

IT'S JUST DARK.

NO NEED TO BE UNNERVED.

SHF

THERE'S NOTHING THAT CAN TOUCH YOU WHILE I'M HERE.

OH... THAT'S MY SMILE.

NOW WHAT WILL I LOOK FORWARD TO?

TP

SHFF

SHFF

•ACT TWO•
CHAPTER SEVEN

Butterfly Weed, Cyclamen, White Clover

I SHOULD BE GRATEFUL SHE PUSHED ME AWAY.

WHAT COULD I HAVE DONE IF SHE HADNT?

I'M NO BRIDEGROOM. I'M JUST THE DOG BEGGING SCRAPS FROM HIS MISTRESS' HAND.

I SEE NOW WHY YOU DIDN'T STOP ME SPEAKING AS I DID!

TIME AND AGAIN, GIVE ME ENOUGH ROPE AND I'LL GLADLY HANG MYSELF.

HA HA HA...

....THERE WAS NEVER ANY HOPE.

GRNCH

...AND I KNEW THAT, DIDN'T I?

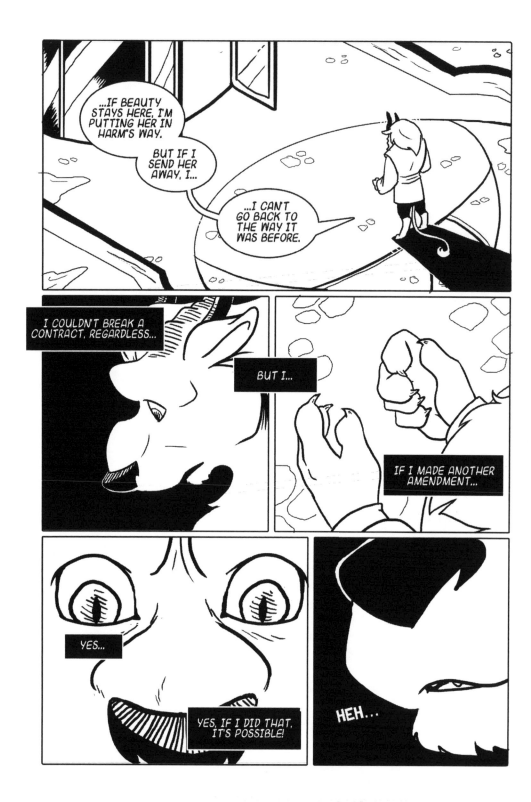

CAN WE PART AMICABLY, OR IS IT TOO LATE EVEN FOR THAT?

Y-YOU MEAN THIS? TRULY?

YOU'RE SENDING ME HOME TO MY FAMILY?

IT WON'T BE...FINALIZED... YOU MIGHT SAY, FOR SEVEN DAYS OR SO... THERE'S ALWAYS A WINDOW...

BUT I...AH... WELL, I EXPECT YOU'LL WANT TO GO SOONER RATHER THAN LATER...

SO IF I WANTED T-TO... ...I COULD GO N-NOW?

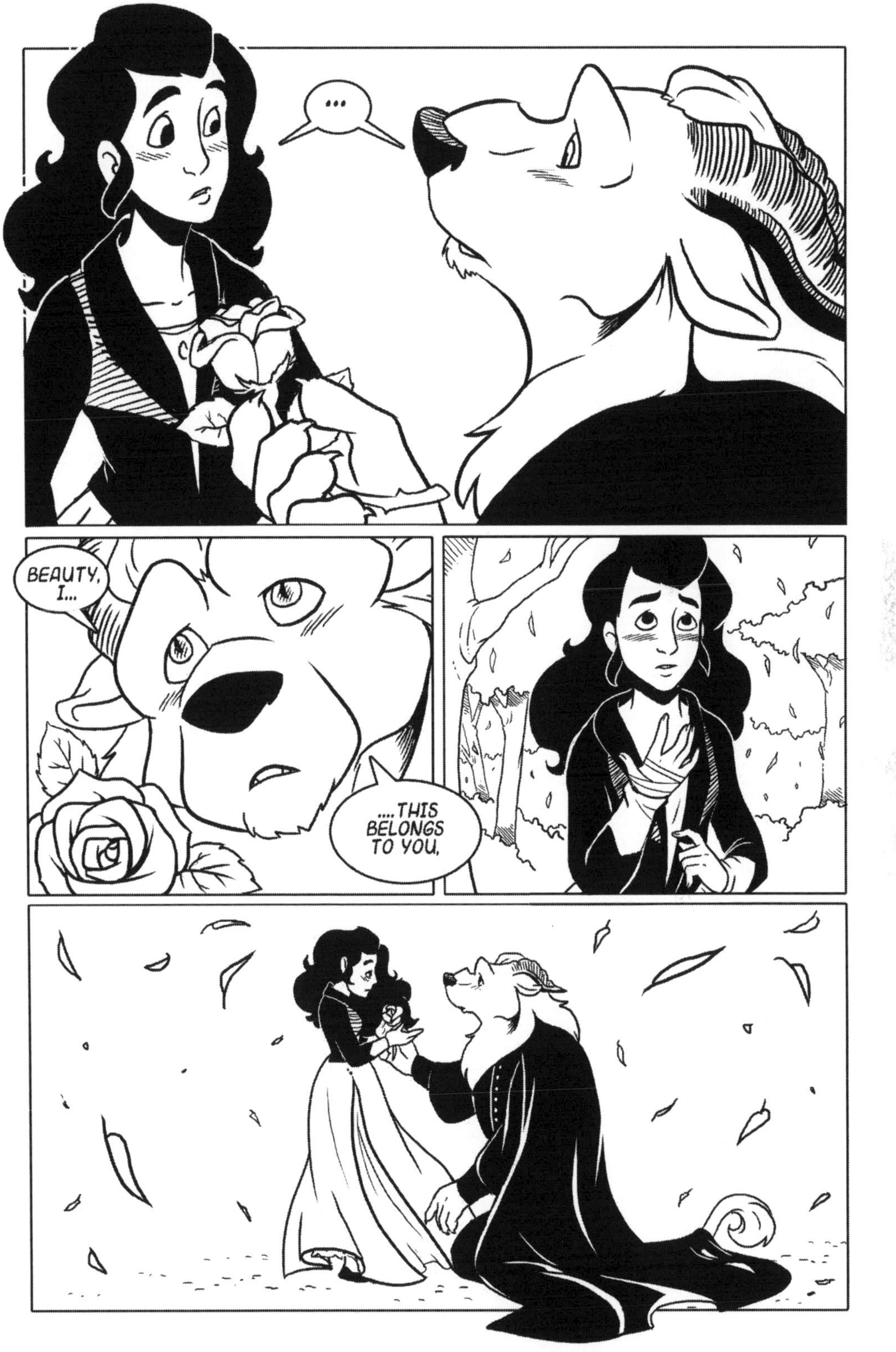
...
BEAUTY, I...
....THIS BELONGS TO YOU,

The Language of Flowers

As in the first volume of *Beauty and The Beast,* the Language of Flowers continues to be a thread running through the story, both in the abundance of The Beast's garden and in the floral studies contained within Argus' herbal. Though meanings vary in every era and locale, for the curious reader, the following interpretations may be inferred

Acacia - Friendship
Adonis -Sorrowful Remembrance
Agrimony- Gratitude
Amaranth - Unfading or Everlasting
Aster - Contentment
Butterfly Weed - Let Me Go
Calendula - Despair and Grief
Chamomile- Patience
Cyclamen - Resignation and Goodbye
Daffodil - Uncertainty
Dark Geranium - Melancholy
Deadly Nightshade -Silence
Enchanter's Nightshade - Sorcery
Hazel -Reconciliation
Houstonia - Quiet Happiness
Hydrangea - Thanks for Understanding
Impatiens - Remembrance
Iris - A Message

Jonquil - Please Return my Affection
Lilac - First Feelings of Love
Oats - Music
Oleander - Beware
Petunia - Your Presence Soothes
Phlox - Harmony
Pussywillow - Motherly love
Sainfoin - Agitation
Solomon's Seal - A Secret
Spanish Jasmine - Sensuality
White Clover- Think of me
Wild Carrot - Sanctuary
Zinnia - Thoughts of Absent Friends

Enfin la Beauté que J'adore

Enfin la Beauté que J'adore is a sentimental *air de coeur* composed by French composer Étienne Moulinié (1599-1676), who was the court musician to Gaston d'Orléans during the Baroque era. It is this song which The Beast encounters Beauty practicing on the harpsichord in chapter two, and mournfully reprises himself in chapter seven.

Enfin la Beauté que J'adore	At Last the Beauty whom I Adore
Enfin la beauté que j'adore Me fait cognoistre en son retour, Qu'elle veut que je voye encore Ces yeux pour qui je meurs d'amour.	At last the beauty whom I adore alloweth me to know in return, That she wishes I once more see Those eyes for which I die of love.
Mais puis que je revoy la beuté que m'enflamme, Sortez mes des plaisirs, hostez vous de mon âme.	And since I see again the beauty that inflames me, be gone, displeasures, get thee hence of mine soul.
Le ciel voyant que son absence M'oste tout mon contentement. Octroye à ma persévérance La fin de mon cruel tourment.	Heaven seeing that her absence Depriveth me of all pleasure. Grants to mine perseverance The end of mine cruel torment.
Mes maux changés vous en délices, Mon coeur arrestés vos douleurs, Amour bannissez mes supplices, Mes yeux ne versez plus de pleurs.	Mine woes, change thyselves into delights, Mine heart, stop thy grief, Love, banish mine torment, Mine eyes, cease shedding tears.

Enfin la Beauté que J'adore

*Original key: C Major

Etienne Mouliné
ed. by Dave Galvin

Tranquille et amoureux ♩ = 72

En -

fin la beau - té que j'a - do - re___ Me fait cognoistre en

son re - tour, En - tour,

Qu'el - le veut que je voye en - co - re_____ Ces yeux

pour qui je meurs pour____ qui je meurs d'a - mour.

3

Mais puis que je re - voy __ la __ beau - té qui m'en - fla -

me, Sor - tez mes des-plai - sirs, hos - tez vous de mon a -

me. me

rit.

Acknowledgements

As always, nothing is created in a void. I owe a great deal of thanks to the many, many people who have made it possible for me focus on this story, and supported me in the telling of it.

Meaghan Carter, Xaviere Daumarie, Nicole Trudel and all the other ladies in the trenches with me at Comic Book Embassy. Thanks for the camaraderie and for making sure I remember to eat.

The wonderful staff at Little Island, Page & Panel and The Beguiling, for their good humour, support and for that amazing book launch. You make Toronto's comic scene happen.

Megan Lavey-Heaton and Isabelle Melançon, for bringing me to TCAF and building the Valor team, and Vanessa Satone and Ally Rom Colthoff for making SPX a go.

My outstanding editor and general go-to story person, Laura Neubert, who once again took on the monumental task of editing this book during her own crunch period.

And always, Nick Hendriks, whose kindness and good nature keep me going. Sorry about all the anime and the crying.

Megan Kearney is a Toronto-based illustrator
and the manager of Comic Book Embassy,
a cheerful co-work studio nestled in the
downtown core. When she's not making
comics, wrangling rabbits, or haunting the
library, she teaches design for animation
at the local college.